The First Christmas

**Illustrated by Jenny Press, courtesy of
Simon Girling & Associates**

The First Christmas

Long ago, in the town of Nazareth, there lived a beautiful and good young woman, named Mary, who was to be married to a carpenter, named Joseph.

One day an angel appeared to Mary. He greeted her and told her not to be afraid and said,

"You will bear a son and will call Him Jesus. He will be a holy child, the Son of God."

Some time after the angel's visit, it was decreed by the rulers of the land that everyone had to return to their own town to be taxed and, as Joseph came from Bethlehem, he and his wife, Mary, had to travel there.

Joseph and Mary were poor so Joseph walked while Mary rode their donkey.

It was a long journey and when they arrived in the town they were tired and in need of a place to sleep but Bethlehem was so crowded with all the people who had come to be taxed that they could find no place to stay.

At last they stopped at an inn and Joseph asked if they could stay there for everywhere else was full and Mary, his wife, was so tired that she could travel no further.

"I'm sorry," said the innkeeper, "but, you see, the town is full and there is no room in the inn."

"Is there nowhere we can stay?" asked Joseph sadly as he held the tired donkey's reins.

"Well," said the man, "there's always the stable, I suppose. It's not much but at least it's warm and dry for your wife."

Mary smiled her thanks and she and Joseph made their way to the warm stable where the innkeeper's donkey and oxen were quietly munching hay.

Joseph made a comfortable bed for Mary in the hay and straw that lay on the floor and during the night the Baby Jesus was born. Mary wrapped Him up warmly and laid Him in the soft hay of the manger.

The donkeys and the oxen watched as He lay smiling up at His Mother, Mary.

In the fields around Bethlehem there were shepherds watching over their sheep and protecting them from thieves and wild animals. Suddenly the darkness of night was gone and a bright light shone all around them.

An angel appeared in the middle of the light and said to the terrified shepherds,

"Do not be afraid for I bring you joyful news. Tonight in Bethlehem is born a baby who is Christ the Lord. Glory to God in the Highest and on earth Peace and Goodwill to all men."

The frightened shepherds clung together as the angel disappeared and the glorious light faded from the night sky and then one, braver than the others, said,

"Let us go down into Bethlehem and see if we can find out what has happened."

So all the shepherds made their way into Bethlehem and found the stable where the Baby Jesus lay in the manger with the animals watching Him.

They found the baby and His Mother and bowed down and worshipped Him. They left a lamb as a present for Him and went back to their fields rejoicing.

Three Wise Men from the East who had studied the heavens followed a star for many weeks because they believed it foretold the birth of a King and Saviour. They went first to King Herod for they thought the birth would be at his court but he knew nothing and asked them to return with news of the baby when they had found Him.

They followed the star further until it seemed to stand still in the sky, right over the stable where the Baby Jesus lay.

The three Wise Men went into the humble stable and kneeling before Baby Jesus and His Mother gave Him gifts of gold and frankincense and myrrh.

When the Wise Men left they were warned by God in a dream not to return to tell King Herod where the Baby Jesus was for he wanted to harm Him so they returned to their own country by another way.

Joseph was also warned in a dream of the danger so he took Mary, his wife, and the Baby Jesus and fled into Egypt where King Herod could not find them.

That is the story of the First Christmas, the birth of Jesus, which happened nearly two thousand years ago and is still celebrated today.